The animal that
appears in Aurora's thought
bubble twice will go with her on her next
adventure in the woods. Who is it?
Which crown
is identical to the one Aurora
is wearing?
A
B
C
D
E
F

Can you find
Tiana's friends, the frog and
squirrel, in the picture of outlines?

Find five differences between the portraits of Tiana below.

Connect the dots to see what dish Tiana is cooking up in her restaurant.

Follow the lines
to see where Jasmine's bird
has decided to land.

Using the two images below, can you complete the sequence?
A
B
Find the real Aladdin by matching one of the pictures on the right to the shadow sitting on the magic carpet next to Jasmine.
A
B
C

Dinner is
served! Help everyone find their
way to Mrs Potts and Chip.

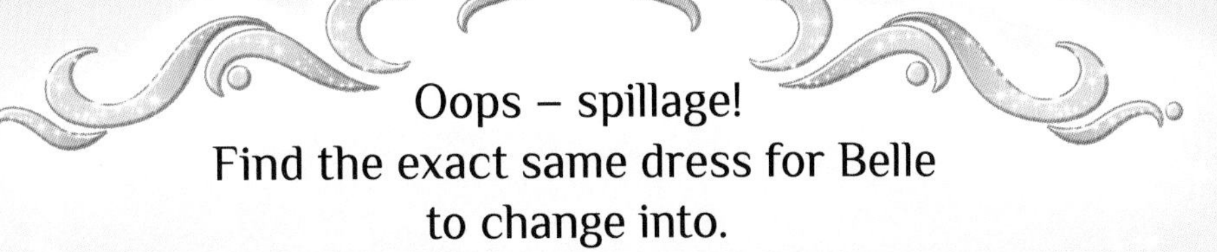

Oops – spillage!
Find the exact same dress for Belle
to change into.

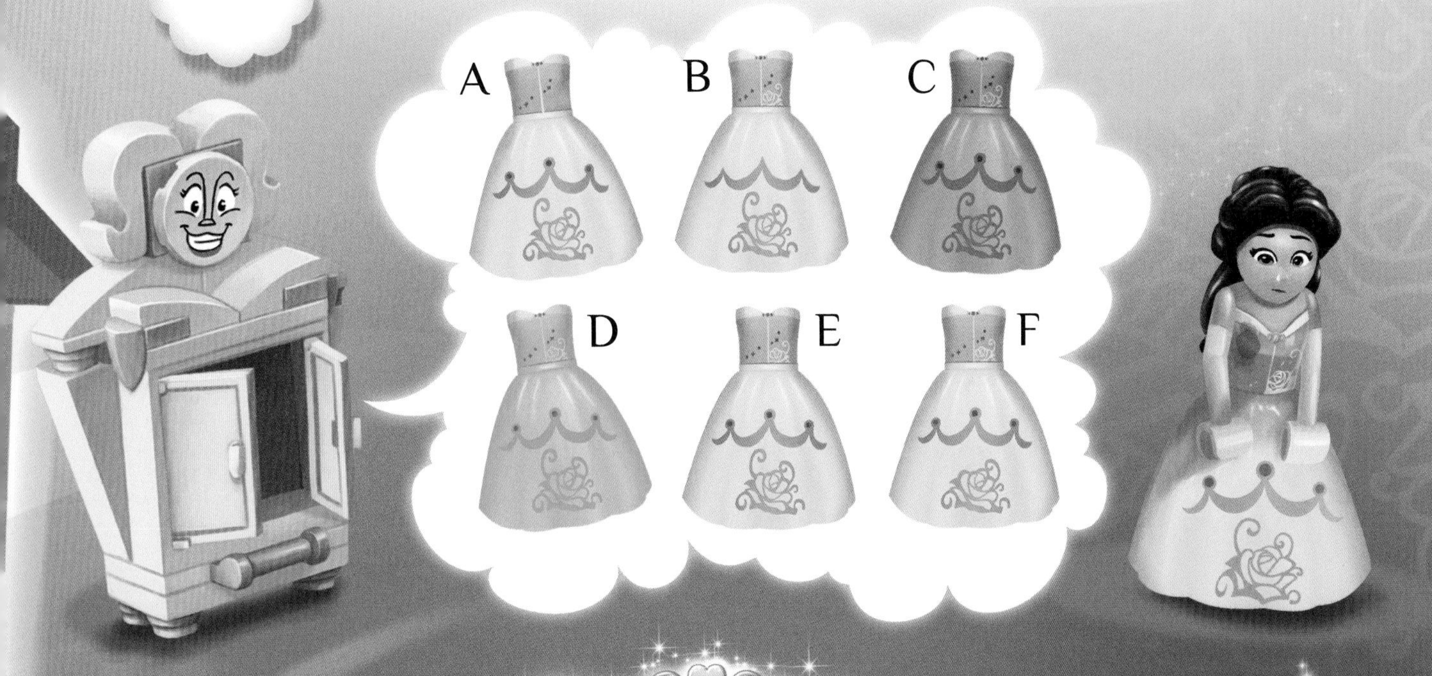

Which of the
portraits on the right is different
from the one that appears in the grid?

Look at the small details and circle where they are in the big picture of Cinderella's beautiful castle.

Which path can Cinderella and the Prince dance along without bumping into anything?

Even princesses have to tidy up. Connect the pairs to help Cinderella put her things away.

Ariel is adding
a slide to her castle! Which slide
shape will land in the water?
A
B
C
D

Ariel wants to build a doghouse for Max. Add letters to the circles to complete the build.

Who can Ariel see through her telescope? Complete the princess's view and colour her friend in.

Mulan knows
that a reflection can be different
from the real thing. Circle seven differences
in the water.

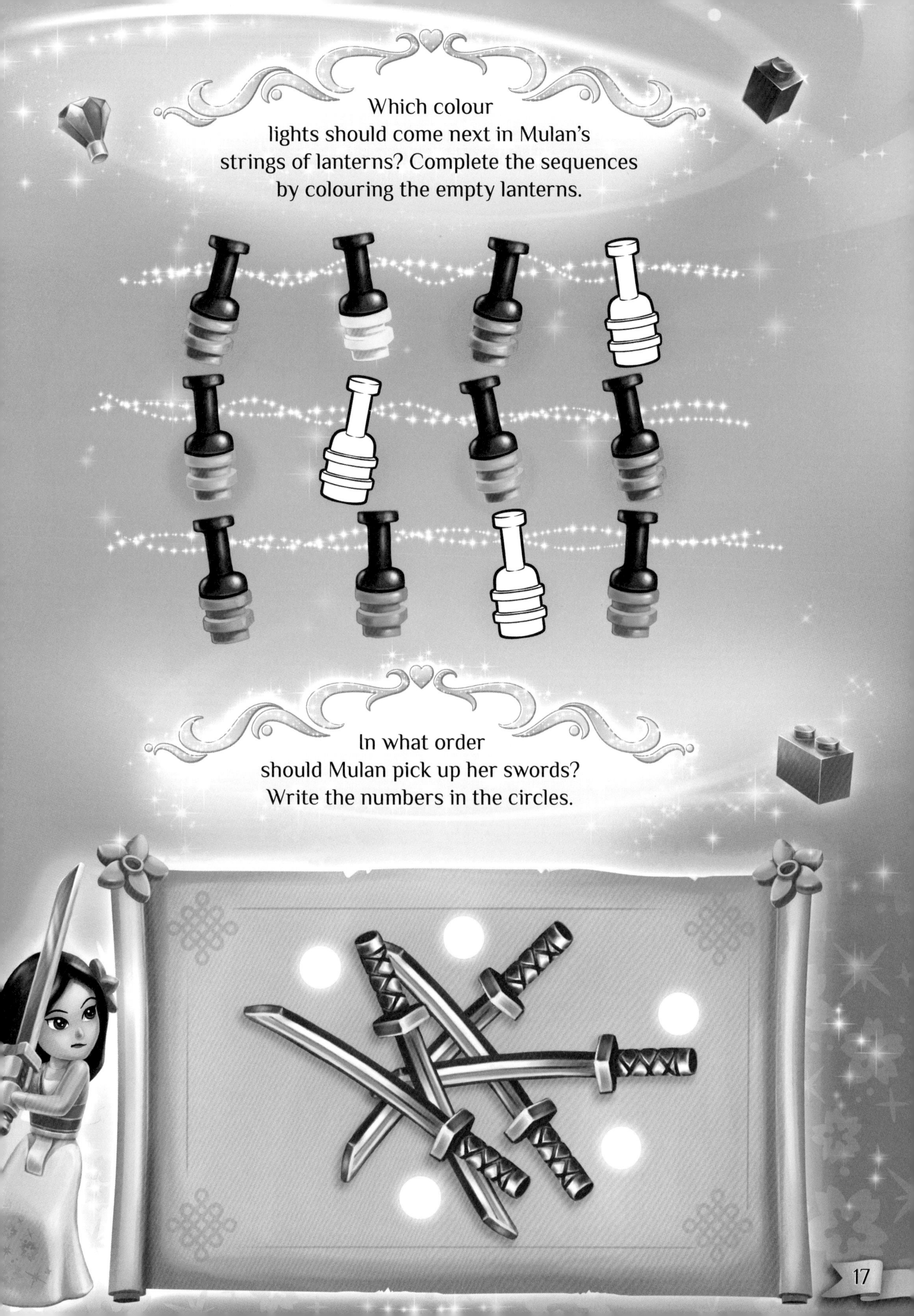

Which colour lights should come next in Mulan's strings of lanterns? Complete the sequences by colouring the empty lanterns.

In what order should Mulan pick up her swords? Write the numbers in the circles.

TIGER TRICKS

SPLASH!
YOU SHOULD'VE JUST TOLD ME THAT YOU WANTED A BATH!
UGH!

Aurora is
sleepwalking! Help her bunny
friend guide her safely back to bed.
FINISH
START

Number the
steps to draw Aurora's crest
in the right order.
Some things
Aurora kept on her bed left
impression marks on the sheets.
Draw a line to each item.

One of the frogs
is different from the others.
Find and mark it.
Complete the
grid with the letters next to the
objects, so that there are four different
things in each row and column.
A
B
C
D
A
D
C
A
C
B

It's time for lunch! Find out what everyone had to eat by looking at the coloured circles next to them and finding ones that match. Then colour everyone in!

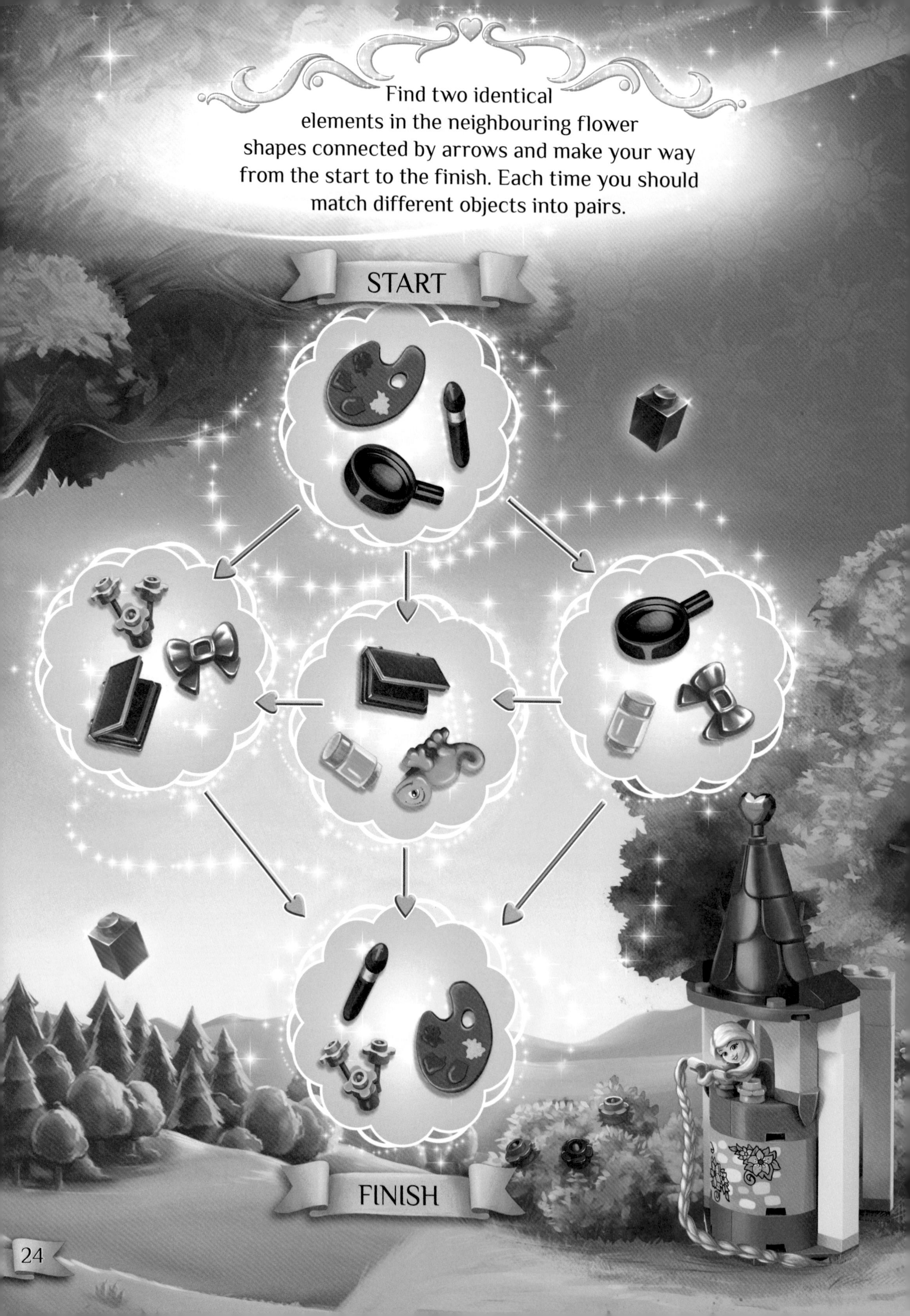
Find two identical
elements in the neighbouring flower
shapes connected by arrows and make your way
from the start to the finish. Each time you should
match different objects into pairs.
START
FINISH

Help Pascal find
his way to Rapunzel.
FINISH
START
Draw an
expression on Rapunzel's face that
matches each description.
HAPPY
SURPRISED
BORED

Snow White is excited to explore this new forest! Draw a path for her so she can weave through the trees to the cottage.

Colour in these trees. What shapes do you see?

Draw two straight lines that don't cross each other and divide the apples into three groups. Then, Snow White, the squirrel and the rabbit will get three pieces of fruit each!

Which books
do Belle and Beast want to read?
Look at their thoughts and find the
books in the library.

Draw the other half of the enchanted rose.

Help Madame Wardrobe put away the pairs of gloves by drawing lines between the ones that are the same colour.

GRAND ENTRANCE

Aurora and her bunny friends are collecting decorations for the castle. "These flowers are lovely!" says the princess, smelling their sweet scent. "They'll make such a grand entrance to the tower."

As the princess climbs up the steps to the tower, the bunnies try to follow her. "Oh, little ones," Aurora says gently. "The tower steps are far too steep for you to hop, but I promise to carry you up in my basket when I've finished decorating."

While Aurora **builds** a floral design at the tower entrance, her bunny **friends below** are building something too ...

"What are you two **busy** bunnies up to?" says Aurora, peering down at them.

"Is that a **seesaw**?" the princess asks. One bunny sits on the seesaw while the other hops down really hard, sending the first one **flying up** into the air and onto the tower **balcony**!

"That's a **fun** way to travel!" the princess says to the bunny on the balcony. "But what about our poor little friend below?"

Suddenly, the bunny pushes a brick over the edge and onto the empty seesaw seat. The **second bunny** comes flying up onto the balcony!

Aurora gives both of the **clever** bunnies a big cuddle. "Now that **entrance** was definitely grander than this one!" says Aurora pointing at the tower.

Which shadow shape matches Jasmine's palace at sunset? Write the correct letter in the empty circle.

A

B

C

D

E

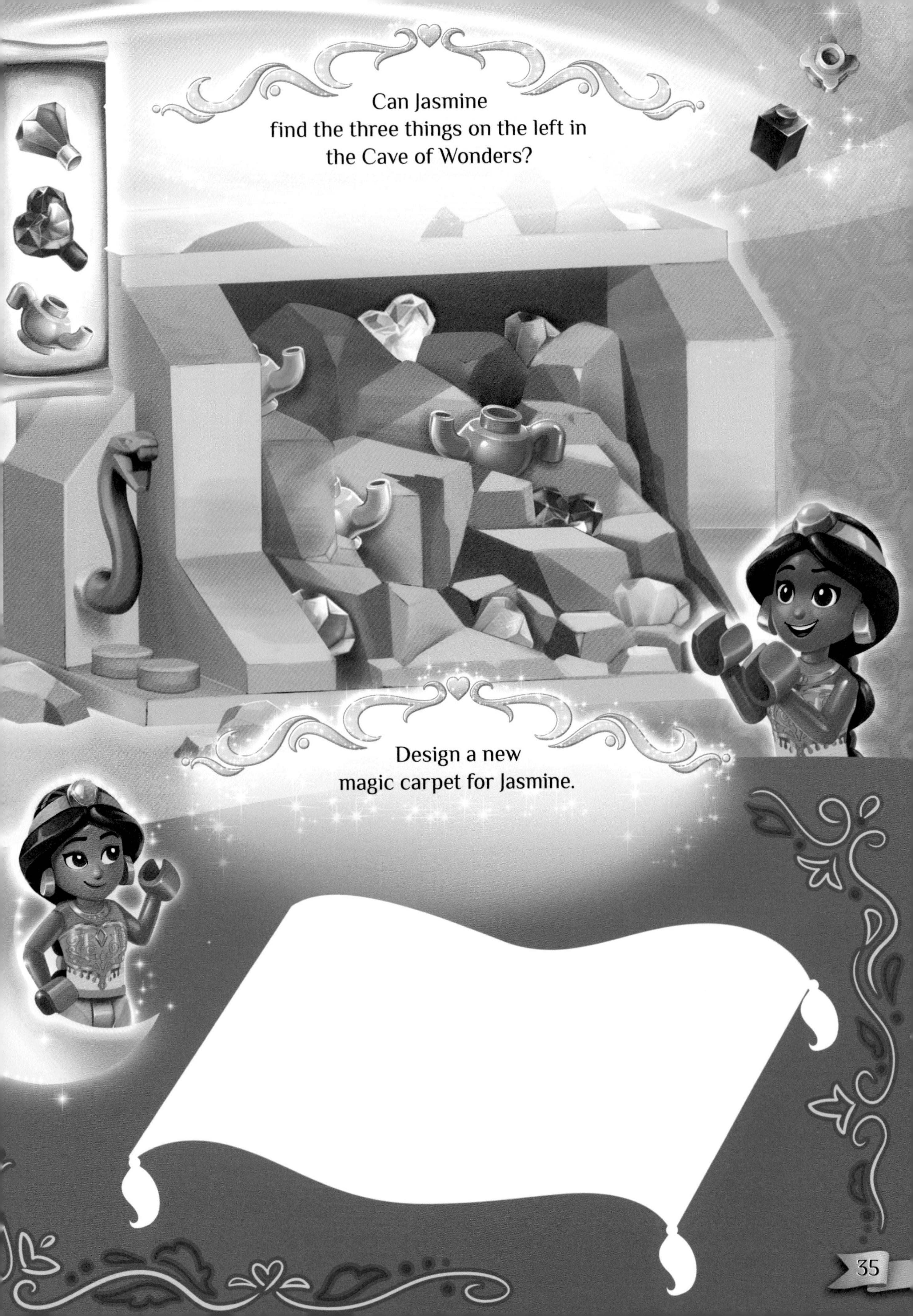
Can Jasmine
find the three things on the left in
the Cave of Wonders?
Design a new
magic carpet for Jasmine.

Tick the circles next to the bricks Mulan will need to make a temple.

Draw a circle around the items you think belong to Mulan, and a square around the items you think belong to Khan.

The amount of water in both buckets needs to be the same. Draw the bricks needed to even the weight inside the left bucket.

Ariel has been out looking for treasure. Guide her boat back to the castle.

Circle the odd one out in each group.

Draw the kind of treasure you'd like to find in the treasure chest.

Take a look at
these pictures of Aurora's castle
and spot eight differences between them.

Use the spots to colour in Aurora's forest friends.

Can you work out the pattern on the spinning wheel? Complete the wheel by writing the correct letters in the empty circles.

Look at clever
Cogsworth's plan to set the table
and draw a line to where each piece of
food goes.
Fill in the
candlesticks as you search for
Lumiere. Can you spot him?

How many place settings can Mrs Potts make? The number of times you can spot the sequence below in the grid's horizontal lines will give you the answer.

   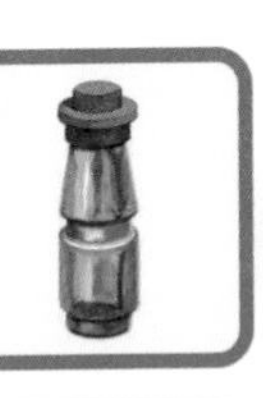    

Draw straight
lines between the same flower
colours to reveal what Rapunzel can see in
the bush.
Follow the steps
at the bottom of the page to learn
how to draw Pascal.
1. Draw an oval.
2. Add a circle.
3. Add a curly tail.
4. Add arms and legs.
5. Add big eyes.

Can you help
Rapunzel find the things
in the purple frame?

ALL TOGETHER NOW

HMM ...
I HAVE AN IDEA ...
TA-DAH!
FINALLY, SOME FUN WE CAN ALL HAVE TOGETHER!

Decorate
Cinderella's carriage by continuing
the pretty wheel patterns.
Help Cinderella
find her way to Lucifer.
START
FINISH

Mark all the
things that Lucifer prepared
for his party.

Look at the small pictures and tick the ones that don't match the big picture.

Use the coordinates below to draw the flight path of the cupcake on the grid.

B1

C2

B3

A4

D				
C				
B				
A				
	1	2	3	4

Guide Mulan through the maze to the cherry tree.

Aurora's castle is almost complete. Draw a line to the pair of bricks that will finish each missing piece.
Aurora's friends are making a dance partner for her. Put them in order from biggest to smallest.
A
B
C
D

Aurora can't decide which dress to wear. Look at the pattern – the missing dress is the one she chooses. Work out what it is and then colour it in.
?
?
?

The owner of this busy stall put out their goods too quickly. Circle the odd one out on each shelf.

How many palm
trees can be made from these
LEGO® bricks?
Find two chairs
that are exactly the same.

Draw a mural
with Rapunzel and Pascal on the
bedroom wall.

Find a path for
Rapunzel to reach Pascal.
Which branch
with flowers on Rapunzel's shrub
is different from the others?

ANSWERS

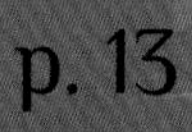

p. 13

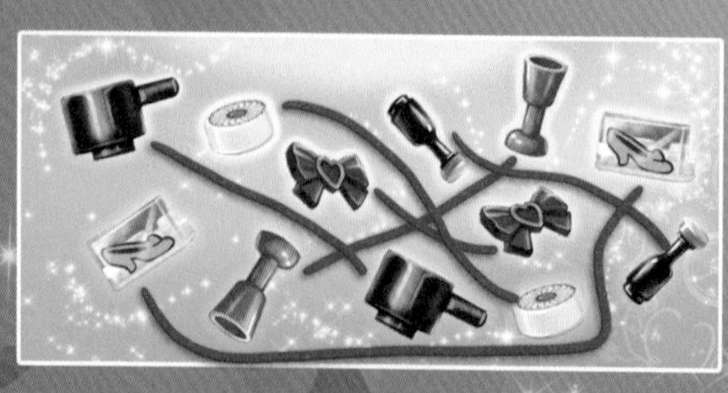

p. 13

p. 14

ANSWERS

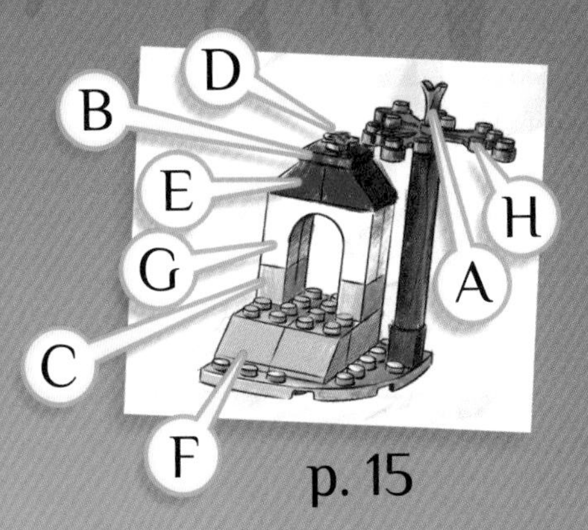

p. 15

p. 15

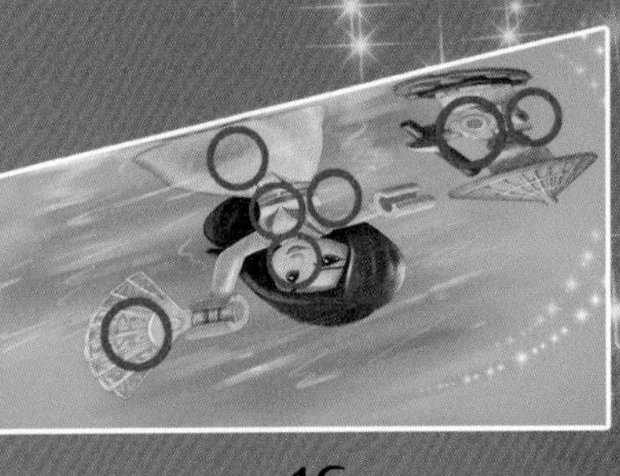
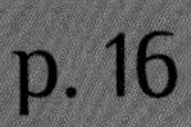
p. 16

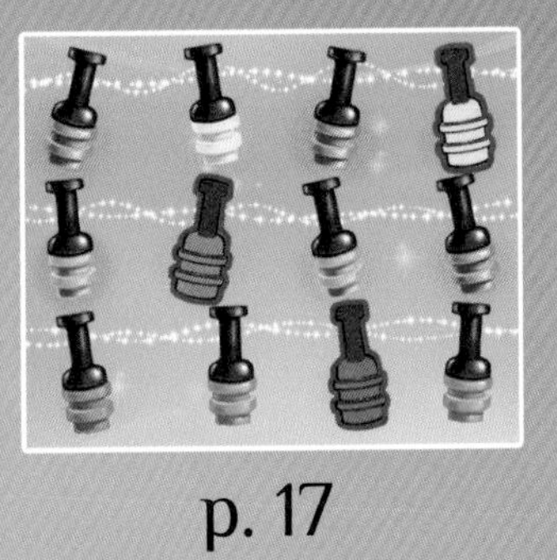
p. 17

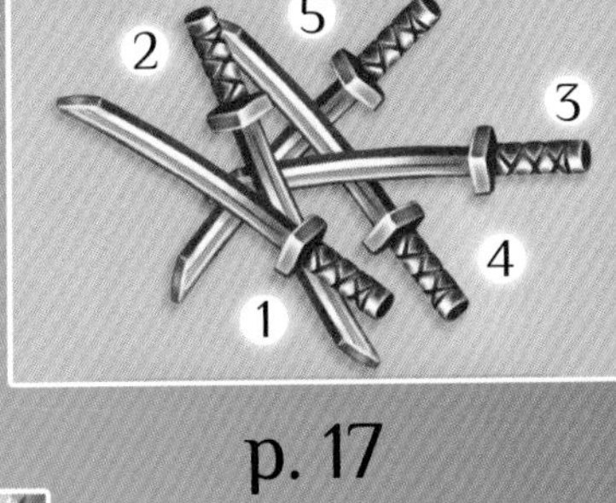

p. 17

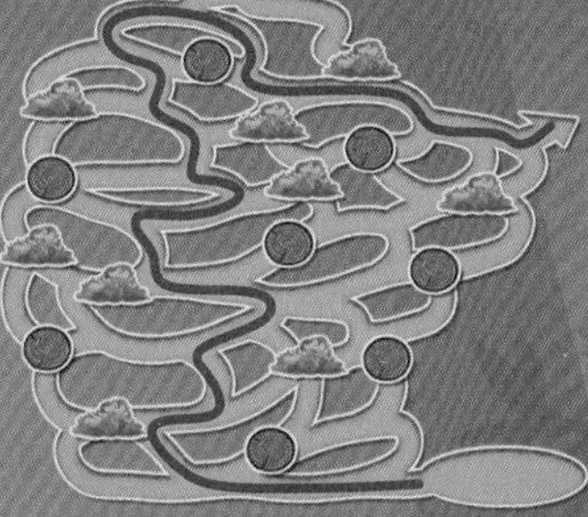
p. 20

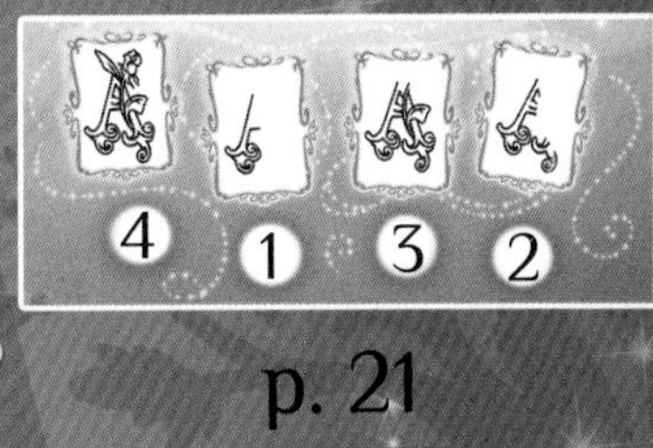

p. 21

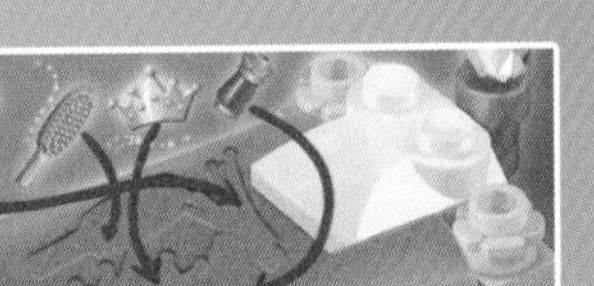
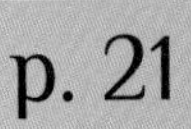
p. 21

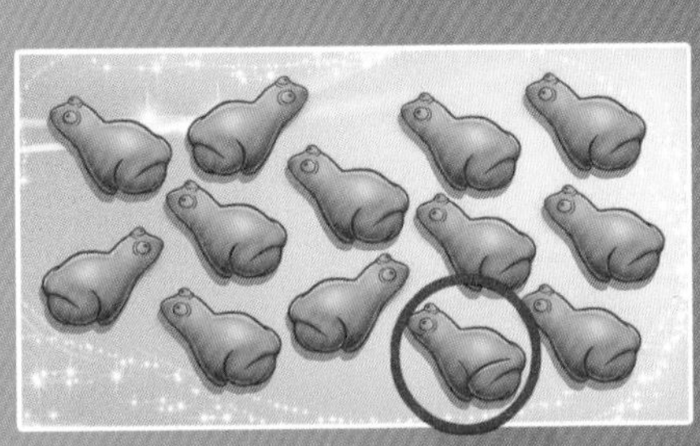
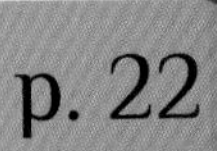
p. 22

p. 22

p. 23

p. 24

p. 25

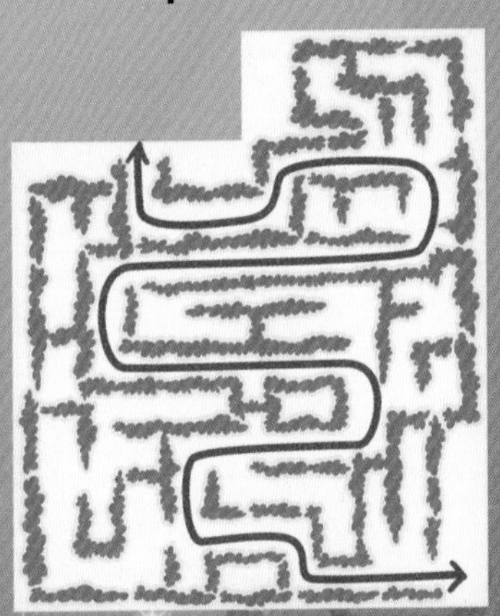
p. 26

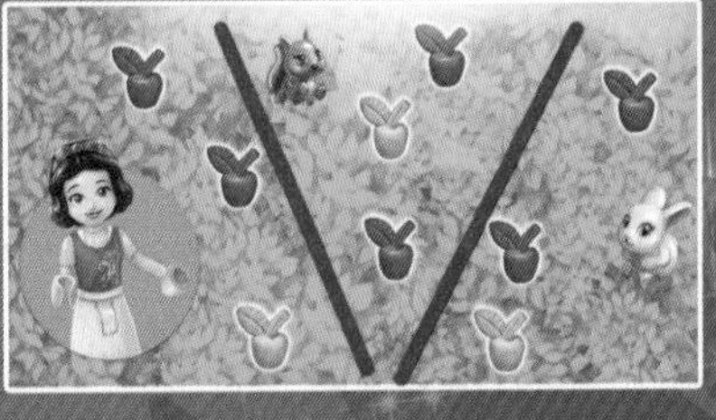
p. 27

ANSWERS

p. 28

p. 29

p. 29

D

p. 34

p. 35

p. 36

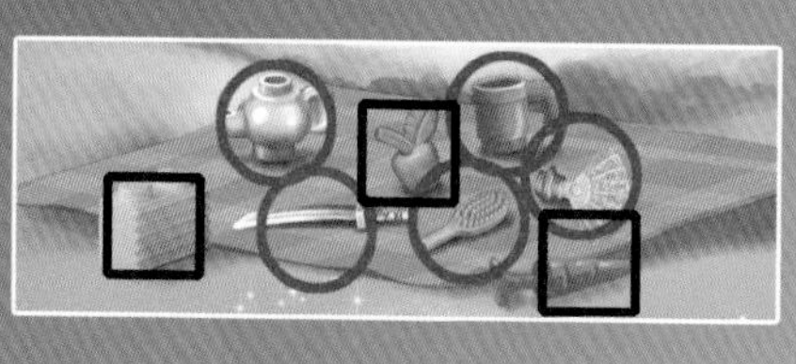

p. 37

p. 37

p. 38

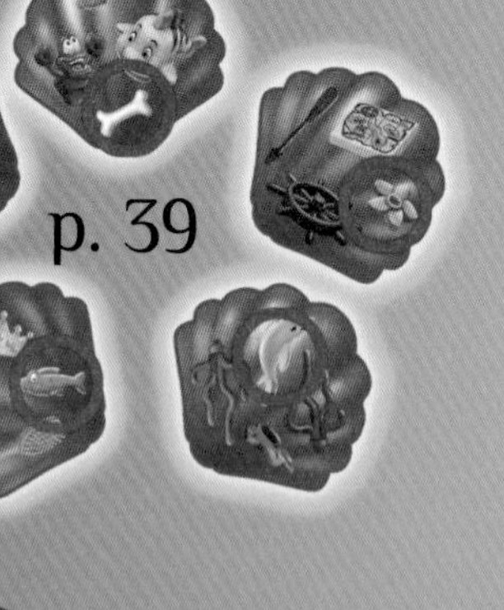

p. 39

p. 40

p. 41

p. 41

p. 42

p. 42

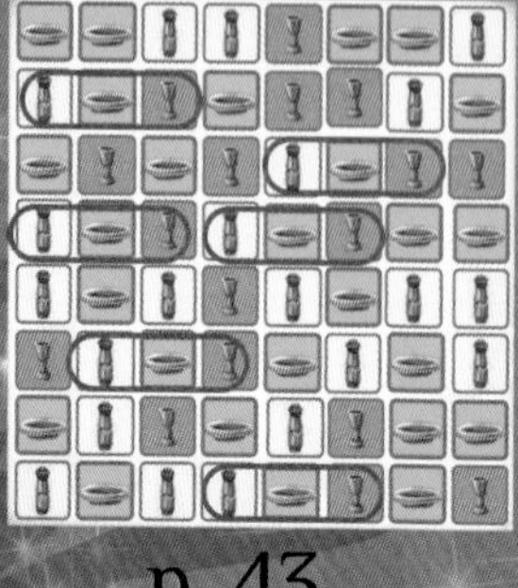

p. 43

6

p. 44

ANSWERS

p. 45

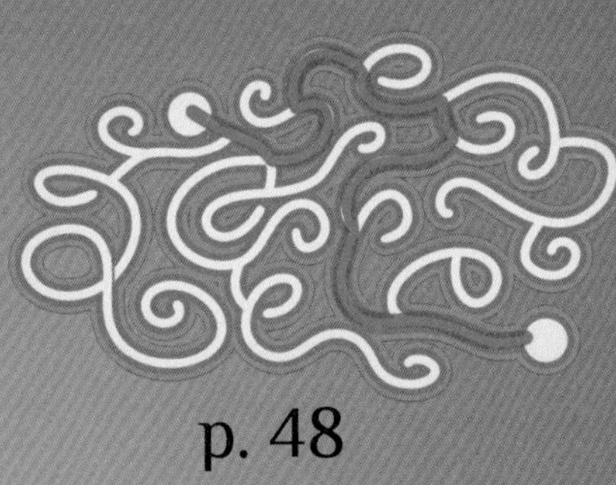

p. 48

p. 49

p. 50

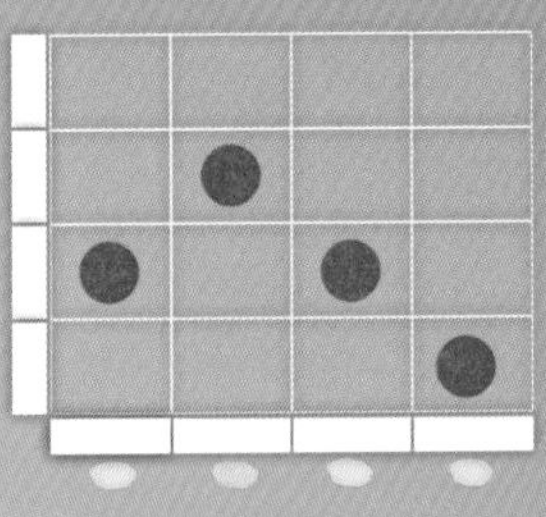

p. 50

p. 51

p. 52

p. 52

p. 53

p. 54

p. 55

p. 55

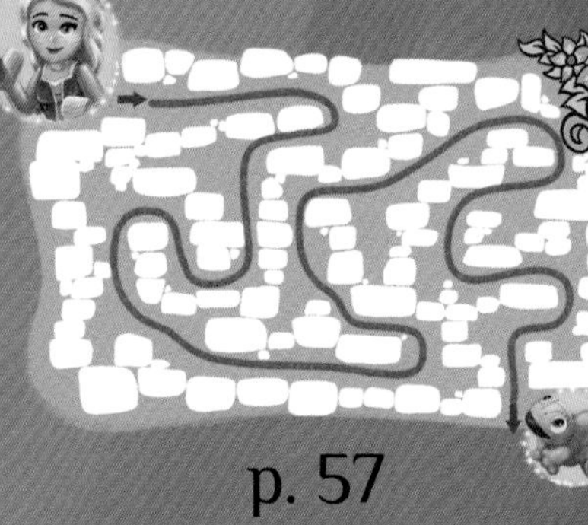

p. 57

p. 57